This SPECIAL STORIES BOOK Belongs To:

_____

FOREWORD

We all cherish our children and nothing gives us greater pleasure than our children building friendships. Through this story we want to raise awareness that children with autism can be your best friend. Thank you for supporting us and the work that we do in building greater awareness in Ireland of autism.

Keith Duffy

KEITH DUFFY, PATRON IRISH AUTISM ACTION

Published in 2009 by
Special Stories Publishing

Member of CLÉ – The Irish Book Publishers Association

Designed by Graham Thew Design www.grahamthew.com

ISBN 978 0 9561751 2 0

A catalogue record for this book is available from the British Library

Printed by C&C Offset Printing Co, Ltd, China.

Special Stories Publishing
www.specialstories.ie

A FRIEND LIKE SIMON

By Kate Gaynor

Illustrated by Caitríona Sweeney

Hi! My name is Matthew and I would like to tell you a story about a friend of mine. His name is Simon. Simon joined my school last year and I remember his first day very well indeed.

When I arrived at the door of my classroom, Simon was standing outside with his Mum. "Hi, I'm Matthew," I said.

Simon's mum gave me a big smile.
"It's nice to meet you Matthew," she
said. "Simon, would you like to say
hello to Matthew?" she asked. But
Simon just turned away and looked
at the ground.

Our teacher told us that Simon would be joining
our class that year. He would take part in most of
our lessons but sometimes he would get help
with his work from a special teacher too.

I thought Simon would like our school a lot. It really is a great school, apart from just one thing, a girl called Hettie, or horrible Hettie as I liked to call her.

Hettie was always pushing her way to the front of the queue at lunch. "I'm next," she'd say when it was someone else's turn and then she would make a horrible mean face.

Every day after we ate our lunch, my friends
and I would go to the school yard and make
up new fun games to play.

On Simon's first day I asked him if he wanted
to join in. But Simon seemed to like being
on his own.

As time went by I noticed how Simon acted a little differently from the other boys and girls in my class. Sometimes he would get upset about something small like someone bumping into him by accident. No one could understand why or even what he was upset about.

Simon always liked to arrange the books and pencils on his desk in the same way every day. He didn't like it very much when anything changed at all. Sometimes he would get upset about things like the school bell ringing or having to move seats.

Because Simon was a little different from my other friends, I soon stopped asking him to take part in games and sometimes I got annoyed if teacher tried to get him to join in. I just wasn't sure if I wanted to have a friend like Simon.

When the time came for the big school trip to the funfair, all the boys and girls had to pair up and find someone to sit with on the bus. "Why don't you and Simon pair together today?" asked our teacher.

So Simon and I sat together on the way to the funfair. Simon took out his sandwiches. "Do you like sandwiches?" I asked him "Do you like sandwiches?" he repeated and then he handed me his lunchbox to share them with me. "Thanks Simon," I said, but Simon was busy looking out of the window.

Later that day, while Simon and I were waiting in the queue for our ice-cream, horrible Hettie marched over to the ice-cream van. "I'm next," she said in a mean voice.

Just as horrible Hettie was starting to push her way in front of us to the top of the queue, Simon suddenly shouted "NO!" very loudly indeed. Hettie got such a fright her pigtails flew up in the air! She quickly turned around and ran off.

"Thanks Simon," I said. "Thanks Simon," he replied looking up at the lights of the big Ferris wheel.

From that day onwards I always made sure to ask Simon if he wanted to have lunch with me or play a game during break time. Some days he would join in, but other days he just wanted to be on his own, which was okay too.

The other boys and girls in school soon learned that even though sometimes Simon acted a little different from us or didn't have a lot to say, he was just the same as everyone else in our school.

Simon helped me to see that leaving someone out because
they are different is something that only
a 'horrible Hettie' would do!

He also showed me just how great it is to have a friend
like Simon! Do you have a friend like Simon?
Why don't you tell me your story?

YOUR SPECIAL STORY PAGE

NOTES FOR GROWN UP'S:

AUTISM IS A condition that affects the normal development of the brain in areas of social interaction and communication. The first signs of autism usually appear as developmental delays before the age of 3.

Autism is described as a 'spectrum' disorder. This means that the symptoms and characteristics of autism can present themselves in a wide variety of combinations and can range from mild to severe.

All children on the autism spectrum are different and although Simon displays behavioral traits common to people with ASD, some other behaviors exhibited may be some or none of the following: Hand flapping, finger flicking, spinning, verbal stimming, hands over the ears, lack of eye contact, toe walking or biting/chewing of clothes/toys.

HOW TO USE THIS BOOK:

WHEN AN AUTISTIC child joins a mainstream school, many children can find it difficult to understand and cope with a student that is somewhat 'different' to them. This story encourages other children to be mindful and patient of the differences that exist and to also appreciate the positive contribution that an autistic child can make to the group.

Irish Autism Action
Raising Standards

IRISH AUTISM ACTION (IAA) was formed in 2001 by a group of parents who took a public stance in relation to the needs and rights of their children. The mission of IAA is to raise the quality of life of individuals and their families affected by autism through ensuring the provision of the highest standards in education, care, support, employment and equality of living opportunities in partnership with families. As well as establishing Ireland's first National Diagnostic and Assessment Centre, Solas, the IAA also have 12 schools around the country. Last April the IAA launched a National Autism Helpline which is operated by parents. It is Ireland's first autism helpline which provides information, advice and support for people with an autistic spectrum disorder, their families and professionals. Keith Duffy is the Patron of Irish Autism Action and works tirelessly to promote an understanding of autism and attract support to help us deliver our range of services. www.autismireland.ie or contact the head office at +353(0) 44 93 71608

Acknowledgements:

Many thanks to the Special Stories Publishing advisory Board, Michael Gill, Sandra O'Malley, Aine Lynch, David Shaw, Fintan Maher, Paul Toner and to Social Entrepreneurs Ireland, Sean, Lynda, Claire and Annalisa for all of their encouragement, advice and unwavering support. Many thanks also to Kieran O'Donoghue, Michael & George Gaynor and our extended family and friends, Liam Gaynor, Liz O'Donoghue, Trevor Patterson, Caitriona Sweeney, Valerie O'Donovan, Lisa Domican, James Fitzsimons and Graham Thew.

Special Stories Publishing is supported by Social Entrepreneurs Ireland
www.socialentrepreneurs.ie

Special thanks to Kevin Whelan, Sarah Rennick and Sarah McEnerney-Buckley and Irish Autism Action without whose involvement this book would have not been possible.

Special thanks also to Dr. Imelda Coyne, Trinity College Dublin whose time and effort with this project was so greatly appreciated.

About the Author:

Kate Gaynor is the author of 11 published children's books. Her titles address the issues of children with special education needs or health and social problems. She works closely with healthcare professionals, psychologists, teachers and families on a daily basis to ensure the quality of her work. Kate is an English and Sociology graduate of University College Dublin and lives and works in Dublin, Ireland

About the Illustrator:

Caitríona Sweeney is an illustrator working and living in Dublin, Ireland. Her passion for art began at an early age and as an adult she studied both textile design and classical animation in university. Caitríona's talent has led her to work on a number of well known children's cartoon series both in Ireland and the U.K

www.specialstories.ie